To Ma

Great news –
Aren't you clever!
Am green with envy.
love
Lorette

Past images drift into the misty
corners of my mind —
fragments caught and held for a
trembling moment —
beckoning me to recall
the child that was me so long ago.

Reflections

by Nanette Newman

with miniature paintings by
Victoria Hamilton

Pumpkin Press, London

These words are for -
Bryan, Sarah and Emma
with all my love
N.N.

These paintings are for -
Nancy and Bobby
to share my reflections
V.H.

First published in Great Britain in 1981 by
Pumpkin Press
113 Westbourne Grove London W24UP

ISBN 0 906946 09 3

Colour reproduction by Culver Graphics Litho Limited Bucks
Printed in Belgium by Henri Proost & CIE PVBA
Victoria Hamilton is represented by David Lewis Artists

Foreword

To try and evoke our childhood past is a desire that exists in most of us, but sometimes we are taken by surprise by a recollection that slips uninvited into the mind.

Perhaps the feel and smell of a summer morning will send thoughts racing back in time - a picture, a word, a touch, can bring sharply into focus a blurred memory of long ago.

Quite often the things we think we will remember all our lives disappear, and the strangest images and thoughts remain, waiting to be taken out, dusted down and jolted back into life - some sad, some happy but all, on reflection, helping to build the structure of our lives.

Katherine Newman

The house was always quiet,
unaware of worlds
beyond its sheltered place
amidst the trees.

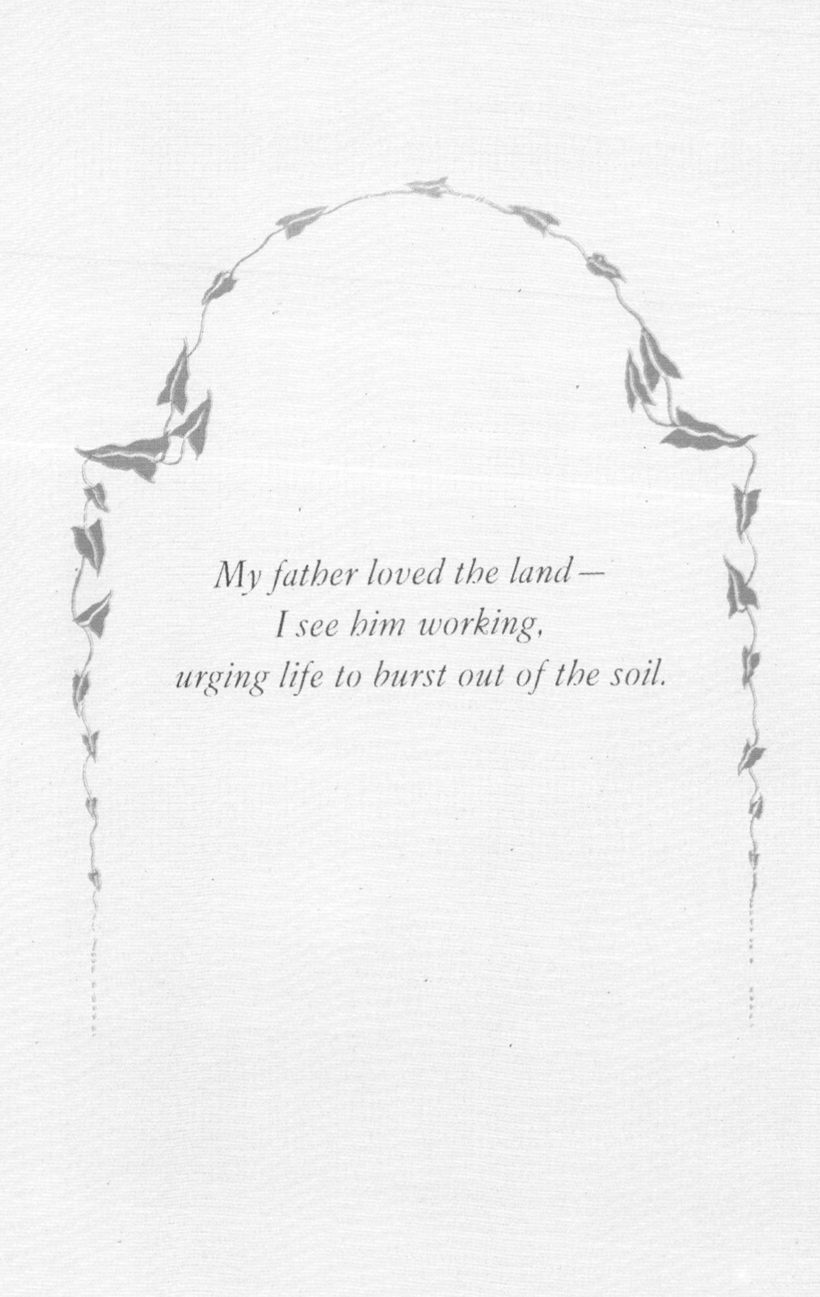

My father loved the land —
I see him working,
urging life to burst out of the soil.

Victoria Hamilton 198

To my child's mind,
the garden was a
place of mystery.

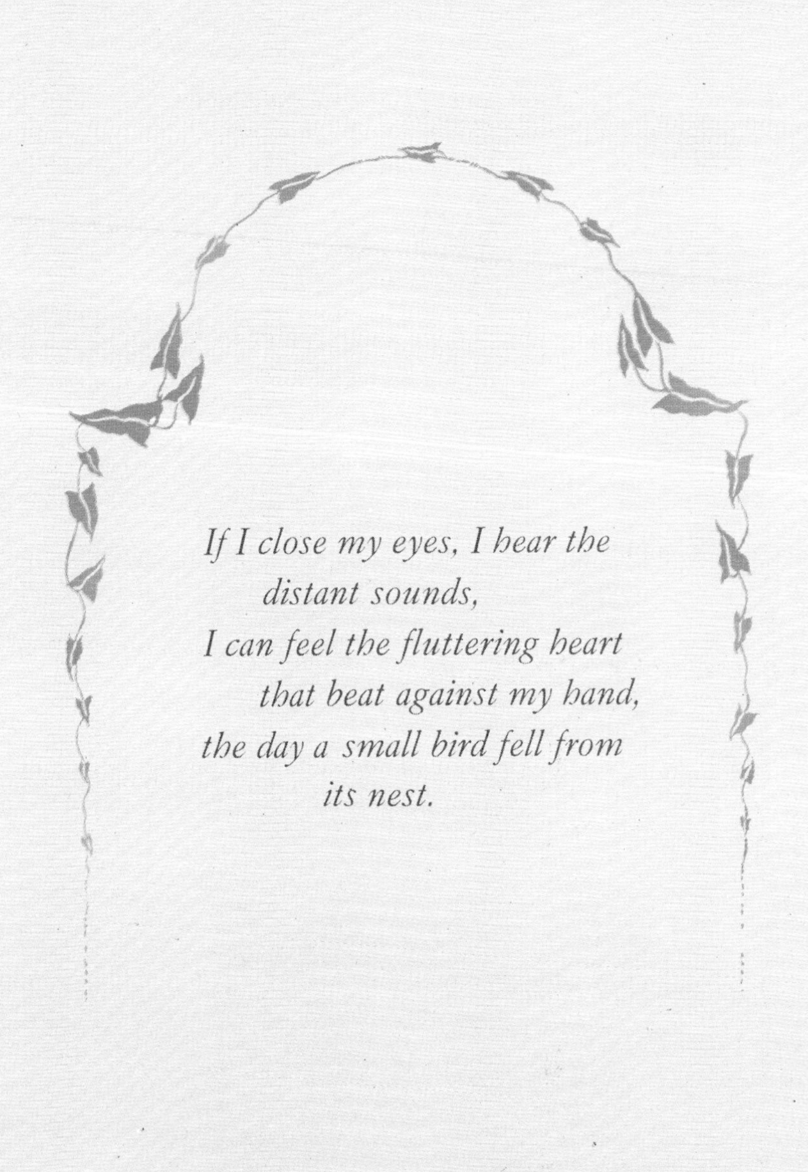

If I close my eyes, I hear the
distant sounds,
I can feel the fluttering heart
that beat against my hand,
the day a small bird fell from
its nest.

I see a squirrel busy —
unafraid…

Creatures watching me, as I
watched them.

Long days, when there was
time to stare and wonder.

FROMANTEEL & CLARKE
10
15
5
20
29
5
25

My father lost his pocket-watch
once.
I searched and searched
until I found it lying amongst
the dandelion clocks...
as if that were the only
logical place
for time to hide.

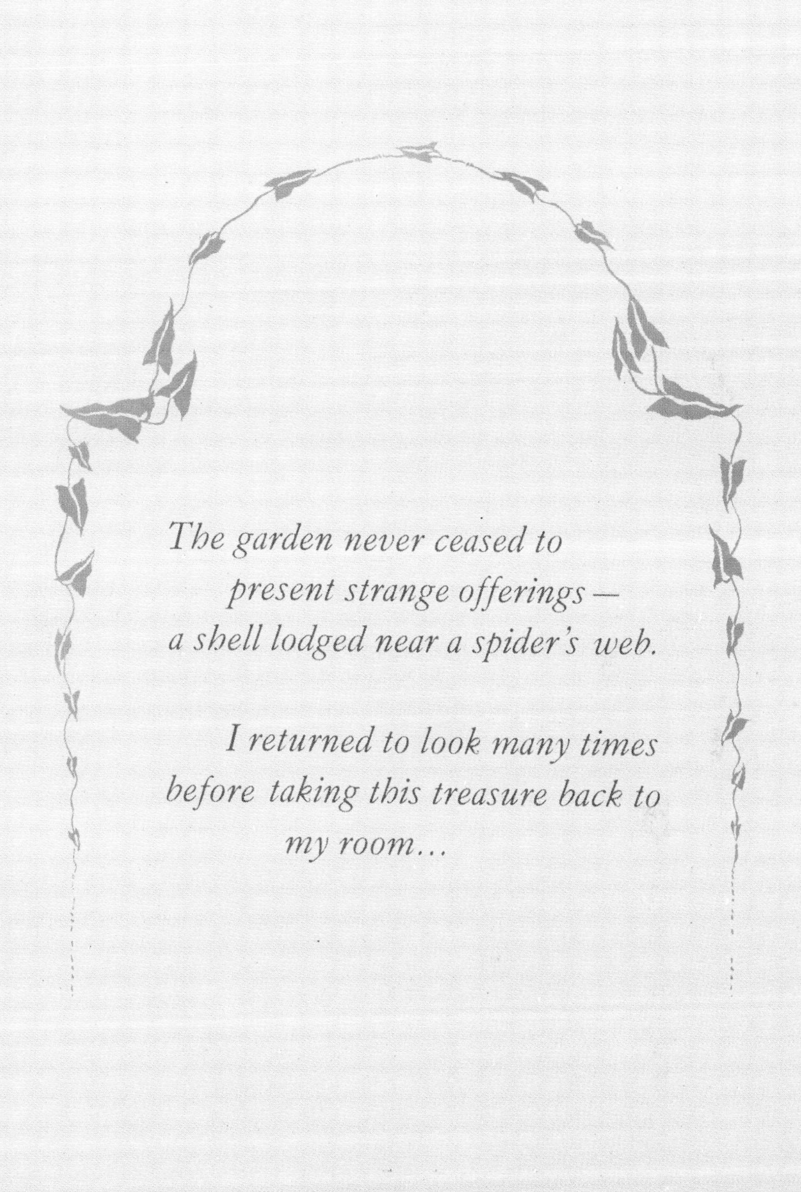

The garden never ceased to
present strange offerings –
a shell lodged near a spider's web.

I returned to look many times
before taking this treasure back to
my room...

I hid it in my bed,
warm and safe beneath
my pillow,
to help me dream about the sea.

I have it still—
I don't know why.

I had a cat once.
He just appeared one day.
I looked out of the sun and there
he was,
his eyes staring from the
dark cool shadows.

I remember strawberries
for tea on summer days —
a first taste
never again re-captured.

My father would take a rest
from work,
and I'd bring him lemonade.

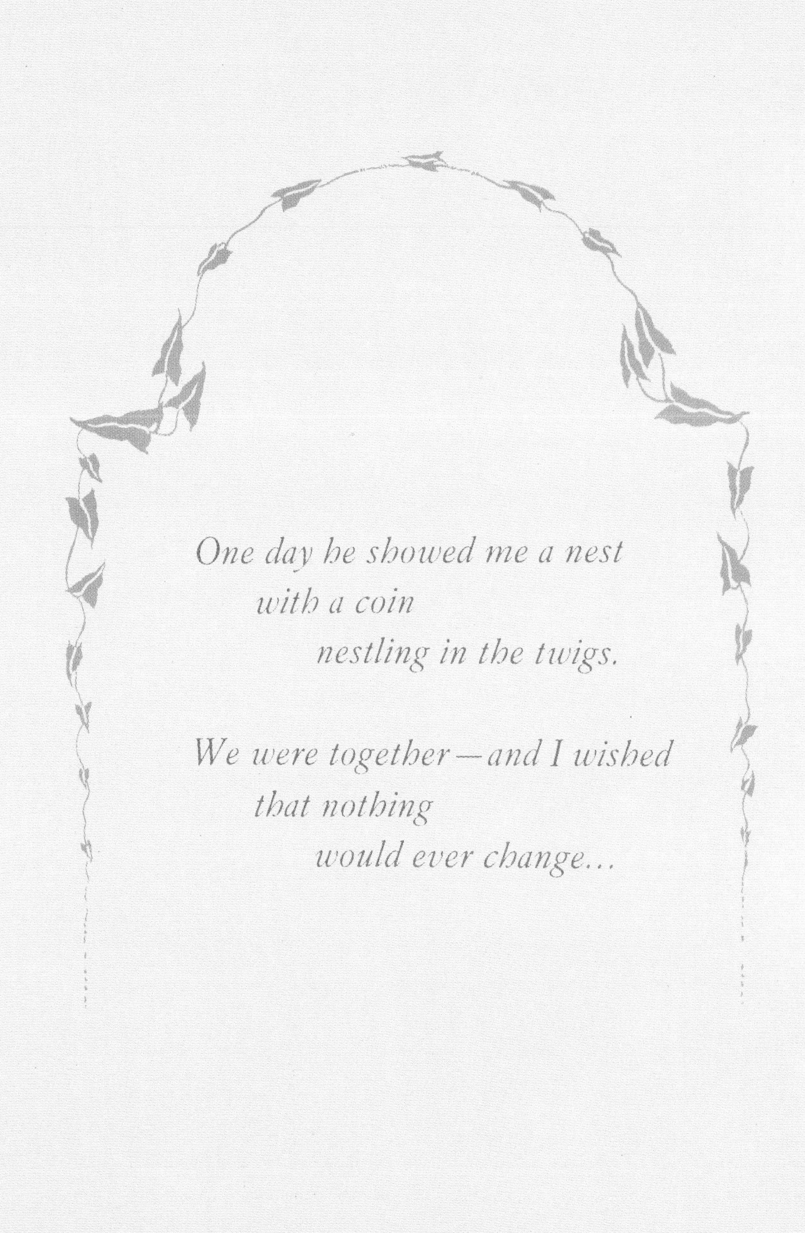

One day he showed me a nest
with a coin
nestling in the twigs.

We were together — and I wished
that nothing
would ever change...

Victoria Hamilton 1980

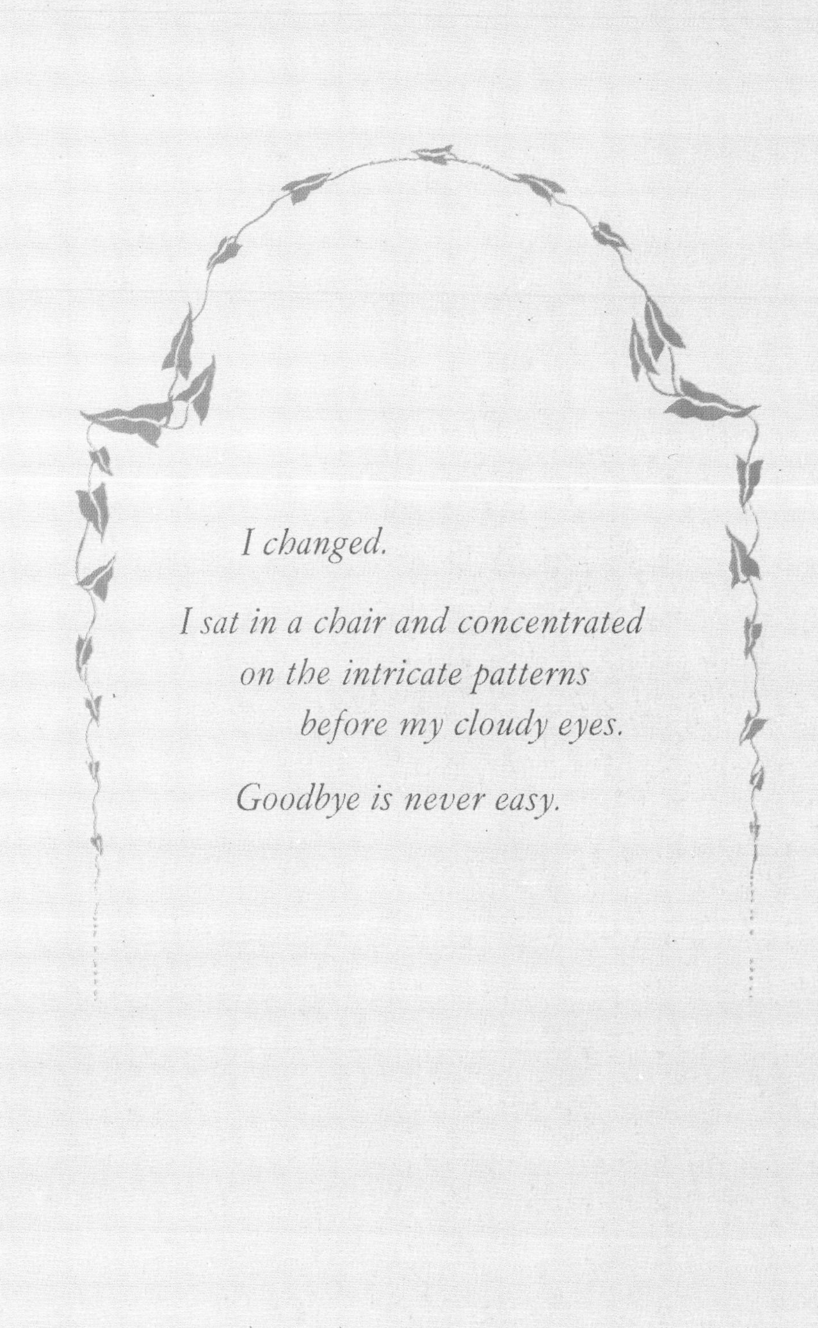

I changed.

I sat in a chair and concentrated
on the intricate patterns
before my cloudy eyes.

Goodbye is never easy.

Saviour of Zion's city I through grace a member am - let the world deride or pity
I will glory in thy name. Fading is the worldlings pleasure. All his boasted pomp and
show Solid joys and lasting treasure None but Zion's children know.
House Near London
Birds of Paradise
Victoria Mary Hamilton May 1980 Aged Twenty Seven Years

Pictures still form in my head—

"I'll write,"

said over a last cup of tea.

My well-known world said
it would wait, while I tried
out life's new experiences.

Everything seemed to stretch
away before me. I never
dreamed I'd think of looking back —
and I went away, of course...

I re-visit my childhood
in my mind,
but the garden is over-grown
with too many memories
of intervening life.

Church
Langley Mill
CLEVE
HUN

LIST OF PAINTINGS
(in order of appearance)

Acknowledgments

The Publishers would like to thank the following for their kind permission to reproduce their paintings in this book:
Mr N. Bointon, *Clocks;* Mr and Mrs Davies, *Captive Shells;* Mr and Mrs J. Eldridge, *Summer Days;* Mrs H. Hamilton, *My Sampler;* Mr and Mrs J. Hamilton, *The Country Gardener;* Mr T. D. Hamilton, *Memories of a Garden;* Mr and Mrs R. Harvey, *The Bluebird, Tea Time* and *Everlasting Life;* Mr R. Lambert, *Twist of Moonlight;* Mr and Mrs P. Mason, *The Secret Collector;* Mr Nasser Abdul Aziz Al Nasser, *The Kitchen Garden, The Winding Lane, Four Poster Dreams;* Mr Saunders, *The Ram;* Mr and Mrs Shaw, *The Watchful Tabby;* Mr and Mrs Simpson, *Nature's Trail;* Mr J. Young, *The Wren's Nest.*

Front jacket flap: The quotation is taken from the poem, *'Reflections'* by C. Day-Lewis, reprinted by permission of A. D. Peters and Company Ltd.